POCAHONTAS

THE TRUE STORY

This is the story of a beautiful princess born four centuries ago. She lived on the edge of an ancient forest in North America, with a vast wilderness beyond.

Her father was a wise and powerful chief, head of the many Indian tribes who lived along the coast and on the banks of the rivers in Virginia.

Now this great chief's name was Wahunsonacock, but it was so hard to remember that he became known as Chief Powhatan, as that was the name of his tribe.

And so four hundred years ago, for that is what the history books tell us, the wife of Chief Powhatan gave birth to a lovely baby girl. They named the baby Matowaka.

One day when the princess had grown a little older, the chief smiled at her and said, "I am going to give you a nickname which means 'playful and full of fun' - because you are such a mischievous little girl. From now on you shall be known as Pocahontas!"

T he seasons came and went. Pocahontas spent a happy childhood in her tribal village on the banks of the river which flowed into a bay with a great ocean beyond. In summer she played with her friends in the creeks and streams. They tried to catch fish with their bare hands and often the naughtiest boys found bullfrogs to make the women jump and scream when they came to draw water.

Pocahontas would wade into the stream to search for terrapins - for they were her favourites - but she was always very careful to put them back into the water.

All the people of the Powhatan tribe were kind to animals. The creatures of the forest were their friends, and the Indians respected all the living and growing things around them.

In the bitter cold of winter, Pocahontas would care for many of the animals who were finding it hard to get food in the frozen forest. Some of them followed her back to the village, and you can imagine what kind of trouble that caused!

The white-tailed deer knocked over the cooking pots and the raccoons quickly gobbled up all the food. Also a family of skunks would follow Pocahontas, and that made the tribe scatter in all directions!

When Chief Powhatan saw all the mess, he simply folded his arms and shook his head. "Pocahontas, you little mischief, I named you well!"

When the winter snows melted and spring came, many of the animals that Pocahontas had cared for would come out of the forest and show her their babies.

The young Indian princess loved the spring when the sun warmed the earth and everyone went into the fields to plant the crops.

"Treat nature well," Powhatan told the tribe, "and it will repay you many times. Plant and water one tiny seed of maize and it will grow into a cob of corn with too many seeds to count!"

Pocahontas listened to her father's wise words and remembered them.

"My father is a great and powerful chief," said the princess one day. "Many tribes honour him and bring him fine gifts. They bring pearls from the river and shining shells to decorate his cloak," Pocahontas sighed, "and I never give him anything!"

At that very moment an eagle soared high overhead. This gave Pocahontas a wonderful idea. Straight away she jumped into her dugout canoe and began to paddle upstream.

Now in her excitement, Pocahontas had quite forgotten the promise she had made to her father never to go upstream. It was a dangerous place through dense woods and dark mountains beyond.

However, Pocahontas wanted an eagle's feather as a present for her father, and the great eagle had built his nest on the very top of the highest peak.

At last she reached the foot of the mountain. The sides were steep and jagged, and as Pocahontas climbed higher, the sharp rocks tore her soft moccasins and cut her feet.

"I will fly up and bring back a feather from the eagles nest!" chirped the little red cardinal bird.

"Let me! Let me!" sang the cheerful chickadee.

"No!" cried Pocahontas, quite out of breath as she went higher and higher. "I have to do it myself. I must earn the feather, then it will be a worthy gift to give to my father!"

It was dark and late into the night when Pocahontas paddled wearily back home. As she rounded the bend in the river she could see the glow of many torches. The braves from neighbouring tribes were searching for her . . . and there standing on the bank, was Chief Powhatan, with his arms folded looking very angry indeed.

Quickly Pocahontas jumped out of her canoe, knelt on the ground before her father and handed him the precious eagle's feather.

"You are brave, my daughter," said Chief Powhatan gruffly. "You are also disobedient!" Then he smiled. "I will accept your worthy gift and will wear it always, my Princess Pocahontas."

S ad to say, very soon the way of life of Pocahontas and her tribe was about to change . . . sailing ships began to arrive from England and drop anchor in the bay.

"Look!" cried one of the Indians. "Giant whales are swimming across the sea!"

"No they are floating islands!" gasped another.

Silently the tribes people watched as small boats filled with bearded whitemen came ashore and began to explore. The Indians met the Englishmen in friendship and gave them food to eat and plenty to take back to their ships.

Chief Powhatan thought they would sail away, but he was wrong. Very soon more came in their sailing ships, to stay and settle around the bay.

In the beginning the tribesmen got on well with the settlers, but wise Chief Powhatan could not help wondering why they had come.

Pocahontas soon made friends with the new people. She played games with their children and made them feel welcome in a strange and different land. She showed them where to find the juiciest wild berries and fruit, and taught them how to catch lobsters and bake clams.

Most important of all, she let them meet her animal friends and told them how important it was to be kind and gentle to all creatures.

As time went by, the settlers cut down many of the ancient trees. They used the trunks to build a large fort and put up wooden houses inside. They called their new home 'Jamestown'.

Soon whole forests began to disappear as the newcomers loaded more and more timber onto their ships. They claimed so much land for themselves that very soon the Indians were left with very little.

All this made Chief Powhatan very angry. "We gave them everything. Why do they need to take so much?"

Then one day a party of braves came upon the leader of the settlers, Captain John Smith, as he was travelling up the river making a map of the Powhatan lands. Swiftly and silently they ambushed him and his men and brought them before angry Chief Powhatan.

Two of the tribes' strongest warriors stretched Captain John Smith out on big stones placed on the floor.

Just as the warriors were about to club him to death, Pocahontas darted out from her father's side. She knelt down and placed her head over Captain John Smith.

At once Chief Powhatan signalled his men to stand back. Brave Pocahontas pulled the man to his feet and he was saved. The Indian braves released all the whitemen and they were allowed to go back to the fort unharmed.

P ocahontas and Captain John Smith were devoted friends from that day on, and the young Indian princess was welcome to visit the fort whenever she pleased.

The Captain often sent gifts to Chief Powhatan, who was especially fond of some bright beads that Captain John Smith had brought with him on his ship.

"These beads get their colour from the very sky above!" joked Captain John Smith, "and they can only be worn by the greatest of all Chiefs!" This made Pocahontas giggle!

Captain John Smith grew very fond of the Indian people and treated them with great respect. Unfortunately many other settlers did not. They were determined to steal all Powhatan land for themselves and drive the tribesmen away.

One dreadful day there was an accident at the Jamestown fort. Captain John Smith was very badly injured in an explosion by a gunpowder blast. He almost lost his life and sailed home to England to recover from his wounds.

Pocahontas hoped that Captain John Smith would return soon, but he did not.

Soon the settlers had a different leader. Captain Ratcliffe was evil and cruel. He didn't understand the Indians at all and hated them.

Chief Powhatan could no longer trust the whitemen who were trying to take over his tribal lands, and so the Indians no longer took corn and food to the fort. The settlers had very little to eat and were beginning to starve.

Peace was at an end and fighting broke out everywhere. Then something very strange happened . . .

C aptain Samuel Argall was sent from England to sort out the mess. After a lot of thought he came up with a bold plan, which if it worked, might bring peace.

He sailed up the river on his ship, invited Pocahontas on board, then kidnapped her and carried her back to Jamestown! Although she had to stay in the fort, Pocahontas was treated like a princess, not a prisoner.

The settlers and their families soon grew very fond of Pocahontas. One of them, John Rolfe, fell in love with her and begged her to marry him, having first asked Chief Powhatan for his permission.

Pocahontas and John Rolfe were married and there was peace between the Indians and the settlers.

No longer a prisoner in Jamestown, Pocahontas was free to walk the forest paths of her childhood. She had a baby son named Thomas and often she would carry him up to the hills above the bay and watch the ships as they bobbed up and down on the waves.

"Thomas," she whispered to her young son, "I hope that one day we may go across the ocean to England!" Little Thomas was far too busy looking at the animals and birds to listen, but before long Pocahontas' dream was to come true.

Many people back in England were fascinated by the story of Pocahontas and how, as a girl, she had rescued Captain John Smith from death. They longed to see this brave Indian princess for themselves.

So one day, along with her husband and young son Thomas, Pocahontas set sail for England.

Pocahontas wasn't the only Indian on the voyage, about ten of the Powhatan tribe took the long sea voyage also. There was very little space in the ship and many people had to spend much of their time below deck.

As a princess, Pocahontas was given a small cabin, but the Powhatan braves had to sleep on the hard wooden floor of the ship.

As the vessel ploughed its way through the waves, it was very difficult to stand upright, and even harder to eat or drink.

As their quarters were so dark and cramped below deck, most voyagers spent as much time as possible in the air above deck.

It must have been an exciting moment when, at last, land was sighted.

What a different world Pocahontas found when she finally set foot in England and was shown the hustle and bustle of the great City of London. There was lots of noise, different sights and sounds, and even different smells . . . and people everywhere!

She saw carriages with horses, church spires and domes that shone in the sun . . . and still more and more people!